Scholastic Literacy Skills

VOCABULARY

Term-by-Term Photocopiables

C000015501

AUTHORS CLAIRE COLLING, VAL GREEN,
CHRIS HOLLOWAY AND SALLY JOHNSON
EDITOR KATE PEARCE
ASSISTANT EDITOR ROANNE DAVIS
SERIES DESIGNERS JOY WHITE & MARK UDALL
DESIGNER MARK UDALL
ILLUSTRATIONS BEVERLEY CURL

Designed using Adobe Pagemaker
Published by Scholastic Ltd, Villiers House, Clarendon Avenue,
Leamington Spa, Warwickshire CV32 5PR
Text © Claire Colling, Val Green, Chris Holloway and Sally Johnson
© 2000 Scholastic Ltd
4 5 6 7 8 9 0   2 3 4 5 6 7 8 9
British Library Cataloguing-in-Publication Data
A catalogue record for this book is available
from the British Library.
ISBN 0-439-01639-8

Contents

Introduction   3
Answers   4
Word Explorer   7

Term 1
Treasure Test 1   9
Treasure Test 2   10
Let's get dressed   11
As time goes by   12
Rainbow words   13
Jumble in the jungle!   14
What are these for?   15
Mystery words   16
S S Sort it!   17
Alpha-bites   18
Animal noises   19
Animal anagrams   20
A body of verbs   21
Now and then, big and small   22
Mini-crosswords   23
Autumn adjectives   24
Friend or foe?   25
All change   26

Term 2
Treasure Test 1   27
Treasure Test 2   28
Winter adjectives   29
Grammar check   30
Discovering definitions   31
Wing words   32
Tiger twins   33
The clues are there!   34
Robinson Crusoe   35
Inside and outside   36

Singular and plural (1)   37
Singular and plural (2)   38
Message in a bottle   39
Copycat!   40
You greedy monkey   41
Re- or Pre-?   42
S-t-r-e-t-c-h   43
Sssh! Silent letters   44

Term 3
Treasure Test 1   45
Treasure Test 2   46
Spot the word   47
Making faces – more adjectives   48
Get into your groups!   49
Delving in the dictionary   50
Well said!   51
Word picture puzzles   52
Getting the message across   53
Star turn   54
Back to our roots   55
Take my place   56
People and pronouns   57
Bridge that gap   58
Linking words   59
Animal alliterations (1)   60
Animal alliterations (2)   61
Use your head   62
How well can you spell?   63

Treasure Chest   64

Vocabulary

The four books in this series are designed to develop children's vocabulary skills through progressive worksheets that are structured to fit the school year.

Written by practising teachers, the content emphasizes the development of vocabulary and spelling based on the word- and sentence-level requirements of the National Literacy Strategy *Framework for Teaching*.

The photocopiable worksheets in each book give opportunities for pupils to work independently of the teacher to enhance their word power. Alternatively, teachers may wish to use the sheets as a focus for whole-class shared teaching, or for homework.

Themes

Each Vocabulary book is loosely arranged on a theme of 'exploration'. This reinforces the idea that children, by exploring and being curious about words, will develop strategies for further increasing their word power. The themes for each book are:

- ❏ age 7–8: Jungle explorer
- ❏ age 8–9: Underwater explorer
- ❏ age 9–10: Underground explorer
- ❏ age 10–11: Space explorer

Word Explorer

Each Vocabulary book contains a photocopiable Word Explorer booklet that matches the theme of the book. The Word Explorer encourages each child to collect new words and learn new meanings by building a personal wordbank. For example, the children may have one sheet on which they write down new words as indicated by the Word Explorer magnifying glass symbol shown on the worksheets. In addition, teachers may choose themes or sets of words related to a topic or particular theme being covered at the time, for example words related to a topic on the Greeks, or a science theme such as 'photosynthesis'.

Treasure Tests

The Treasure Test words are target words that children should learn. There are six pages of these in each book, two for each term, which children can take home to learn (see pages 9, 10, 27, 28, 45 and 46). They can test their knowledge of Treasure Test words at the end of each term with the Treasure Chest sheet on page 64. Teachers may choose to use this as an assessment guide in the form of a test or, alternatively, children of similar ability could test each other to reinforce their knowledge. The Treasure Tests are progressive and consolidatory – that is, the word lists for ages 8–9 revise and consolidate vocabulary from the ages 7–8 Vocabulary book, and so on. The Children may wish to keep the Treasure Test sheets and Word Explorer booklets in their own personal folders or portfolios.

Answers

These are given on pages 4–6. Some activities are open-ended and, where appropriate, suggestions are provided.

Guide to symbols used

 = magnifying glass. This denotes new or challenging words which should be added to the Word Explorer booklet.

 = dictionary/thesaurus. This symbol indicates children will need to use a dictionary and/or thesaurus to complete the task.

 = Treasure Chest. The Treasure Chest symbol denotes more challenging tasks which may be suitable for extension work.

Answers

Let's get dressed (page 11)

My body: head, foot, neck, hand, waist, legs.
My clothes: glove, belt, scarf, trousers, sock, hat.
Pairs: foot – sock; hand – glove; neck – scarf;
waist – belt; legs – trousers; hat – head.

As time goes by (page 12)

Days of the week: Monday, Tuesday, Wednesday,
Thursday, Friday, Saturday, Sunday. Months of the
year: January, February, March, April, May, June, July,
August, September, October, November, December.
Seasons: spring, summer, autumn, winter.

Rainbow words (page 13)

Word puzzle (in any order): 1. black 2. grey 3. brown
4. purple 5. pink 6. red 7. blue 8. green 9. white.
Sentences (a): 1. black 2. red 3. black, white 4. green
5. blue; (b): 1. pink/red/white/yellow etc (variable)
2. brown (variable) 3. gold/yellow 4. white 5. red,
white, blue.

Jumble in the jungle (page 14)

In order: short; tall; long; lovely, colourful; wide.

What are these for? (page 15)

1–6. Children's own answers obtained by referring to
dictionaries.
Choose the correct word: 1. end 2. beginning.

Mystery words (page 16)

Answers will vary according to which dictionary is
referred to. Possible answers are: seldom – rarely;
grazing – eating; aroma – smell, scent, fragrance;
plumage – feathers; foliage – leaves; dense – thick.

Sort it! (page 17)

about; ball; came; did; eight; first; got; has; if; jump;
kite; last.
m–z: children's own answers.

Alpha-bites (page 18)

1. banana 2. bed 3. biscuit 4. boy 5. bun.
Food words: banana, biscuit, bun.

Animal noises (page 19)

chattering; buzzing; purring; hissing. cat, purring;
bee, buzzing; snake, hissing; monkey, chattering.
hopped; creeping; fluttering.

Animal anagrams (page 20)

parrot; butterfly; alligator; gorilla.

A body of verbs (page 21)

In order: laughing, shouting, crying, kissing, thinking
waving, pointing, catching, carrying, hugging,
dancing, kneeling, jumping, kicking, sitting.

Now and then, big and small (page 22)

Present: 1. man 2. frog 3. hen 4. grows 5. jumps
6. butterfly 7. Swans, have.
Past: 1. saw 2. swam 3. walked 4. acorn 5. foal,
jumped 6. caught, caterpillar 7. had.

Mini-crosswords (page 23)

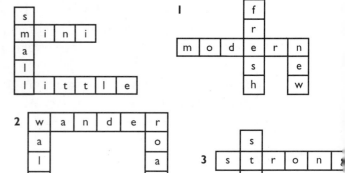

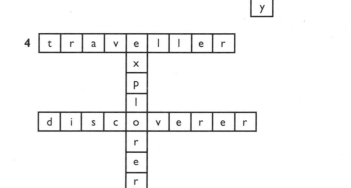

Autumn adjectives (page 24)

In order: crisp/beautiful; Golden; tall; grey; leafy;
comfortable; Red; brown; beautiful/crisp; prickly;
musty; migrating; warmer.

Friend or foe? (page 25)

Words beginning speech (red): said; asked; replied.
Words ending speech (blue): promised; shouted;
exclaimed; squawked.

All change (page 26)

un: unwise; uneven; untidy; undress; unfriendly.
dis: dishonest; dismount; disuse; distrust.

Winter adjectives (page 29)

The children's descriptions should demonstrate
appropriate use of the adjectives and nouns listed,
and use of sentences and correct punctuation.

Grammar check (page 30)

Sentence – A group of words that makes sense, and
begins with a capital letter and ends with a full stop,
question mark or exclamation mark. Noun – A
naming word. Singular – A single item. Prefix – A
group of letters that can be placed at the beginning of
a word to change its meaning. Suffix – A group of
letters added to the end of a word that changes its
meaning. Plural – More than one. Adjective – A word
that describes a noun. Verb – An action word.

Discovering definitions (page 31)

1. chair 2. tricycle 3. clock 4. hippopotamus 5. orange 6. wellington boots.

Wing words (page 32)

In any order: heel – heal; dear – deer; bury – berry; hole – whole; bear – bare; due – dew; blew – blue; sell – cell; our – hour.

Tiger twins (page 33)

1. moan 2. knew 3. saw 4. pain 5. prey 6. slay 7. scent 8. scene 9. weak 10. some.

The clues are there! (page 34)

slithering – snake; lumbering – elephant; snapping – crocodile; colourful – parrot.
Children's own answers.

Robinson Crusoe (page 35)

Nouns (red): Robinson Crusoe; ship; island; sands; home; caves; raft; trees; forest; raft; food; tools; wreck; axe; fence; animals; plans; grapes; bananas; forest; grains; rice; wheat; ship; goats; meat; milk.
Adjectives (blue): sailing; lonely; desert; silver; comfortable; rocky; strong; palm; dense; dry; useful; sinking; sharp; tall; fierce; juicy; ripe; green; plump; wild; fresh; creamy.

Inside and outside (page 36)

Cupboard; tablecloth; window-sill; lampshade; bathroom; doorstep. Playground; snowflake; seaside; sunshine; thunderstorm; raindrop.
Suggestions for new words (answers variable): houseboat; homework; earthquake; afternoon; daylight; somewhere; seashore; toothache; lighthouse.

Singular and plural (1) (page 37)

1 fern, 4 ferns; 1 parrot, 2 parrots; 1 frog, 3 frogs; 1 flower, 5 flowers.
To change the singular words into their plurals I have had to add an s.
Three bunches of flowers. Two thorny branches. Five rose bushes. Four broken glasses. Seven cardboard boxes. Six sandy beaches.
I have had to add es to nouns ending in ch, ch, ss and x.

Singluar and plural (2) (page 38)

Fly – Flies; Baby – Babies; City – Cities; Lady – Ladies; Fairy – Fairies; Lorry – Lorries; Knife – Knives; Leaf – Leaves; Loaf – Loaves; Wolf – Wolves; Potato – Potatoes; Tomato – Tomatoes.
child; man; foot; woman; goose; tooth.

Message in a bottle (page 39)

In order: muddle; scramble; puddle; little; bottle; bottle; puzzle.

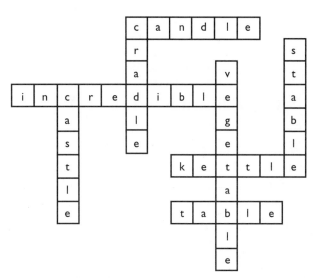

Copycat! (page 40)

happy – glad; sad – unhappy; shout – yell; great – wonderful. Children's own answers.

You greedy monkey (page 41)

1. I am 2. can not 3. do not 4. I will 5. who is 6. are not 7. I have 8. should not.

Re- or Pre-? (page 42)

1. repeat 2. prepared 3. rebuilt 4. prevent 5. repot 6. prescribed 7. remake 8. prefixes 9. reload.

S-t-r-e-t-c-h (page 43)

1. playful 2. mouthful 3. restful 4. useful 5. careless 6. cheerless 7. fearless 8. spotless 9. quickly 10. loudly 11. bravely 12. brightly.

Ssh! Silent letters (page 44)

writing; knight; knife; wrestling; wrong; knitting; gnashing; gnaw; wriggle; wrap; kneeling; gnome; wring; knob; gnat.

Spot the word (page 47)

In order: singing; slithered; chattered; crawled; opened; crept; boomed; fall; shining; hurried.

Making faces — more adjectives (page 48)

Anna: long/narrow; curly; drooping; sad; pointed.
Sophie: long; straight; large; smiling; happy; freckled.
Ashley: furious; round/large; plump; tiny; short; spiked.
Chandani: pretty; long; plaited; sparkling.

Get into your groups! (page 49)

mislead; antibody; co-education; misplace; co-operate; export; antiseptic; co-exist; extend; mistake; exchange; antisocial.
ex-: extend; export; exchange. mis-: mislead; mistake; misplace. co-: co-operate, co-education, co-exist. anti-: antibody; antiseptic; antisocial.

Answers may vary depending upon the dictionary used but should be something like: co-operate – work together; extend – make larger or longer; antiseptic – sterile, free from contamination; mistake – incorrect idea, a thing incorrectly done.

Delving in the dictionary (page 50)

Children's own answers.

Well said! (page 51)

1. roared 2. whispered 3. cried/squealed 4. cheered 5. yelled 6. called 7. squealed/cried 8. muttered 9. reported 10. laughed.

Word picture puzzles (page 52)

1. watch 2. saw 3. bank.
wave; stamp.

Getting the message across (page 53)

Warning: Look out!; Beware!; Watch it!; Take care.
Suprise: Wow!; What!; Well I never!; Really?
Thank you: Much appreciated; Ta.
Apology: Pardon me; Excuse me; I'm sorry.
Disappointment: Oh dear; Oh no!; It can't be.
Greeting: How do you do?; Hello; Good morning; Hi; Welcome; Pleased to meet you.
Refusal: Go away; I'd rather not; Not really; No.

Star turn (page 54)

In any order: co-operate; misunderstand; nonsense; anticlockwise; export.
Children's own answers obtained by looking in dictionaries.

Back to our roots (page 55)

immortal; nonsense; afternoon; displeased; irregular; misfortune; unlucky.
Children's own answers.

Take my place (page 56)

In order: them; him; She; it.
They; they; it; She; them.

People and pronouns (page 57)

He; She; them; him; they.
Children's own answers.

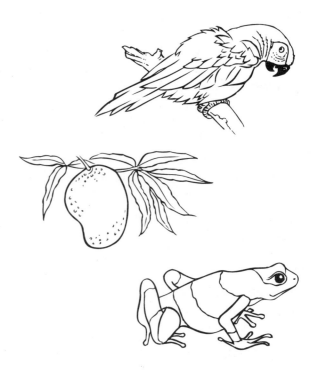

Bridge that gap (page 58)

1. answer on sheet 2. I enjoy fishing though/but I am not very patient. 3. You may see a kingfisher if you are lucky. 4. My dog waits patiently while I prepare my fishing line. 5. My dog likes to accompany me so/when/if he can run along the bank. 6. I stay in my pitch until I catch a fish. 7. Fish feed best at dawn though/but my best catch was in the evening. 8. My brother has not been with me since he tripped over my fishing line.

Linking words (page 59)

1. because/as/since 2. while/as/because 3. if/when 4. and/then 5. while/as/and 6. since/because/as 7. though/but/and.

Animal alliterations (1) (page 60)

mischievous monkeys; slithering snakes; stinging scorpion; spinning spiders; crawling crocodile; darting dragonflies; lazy lizards; angry alligator; prickly porcupines; beautiful butterflies; buzzing bees; chattering chimpanzees.

Animal alliterations (2) (page 61)

1. Beautiful butterflies 2. angry alligator 3. Slithering snakes 4. stinging scorpion 5. Lazy lizards 6. Spinning spiders 7. Prickly porcupines 8. Chattering chimpanzees.

Use your head (page 62)

head: bread; dead; lead; tread; dread.
tear: ear; fear; hear; dear; year.

How well can you spell? (page 63)

Mistakes and corrections (in order): litle – little; four – for; forrest – forest; somethink – something; slowley – slowly; banck – bank; makeing – making; thort – thought; mite – might; sore – saw; scard – scared; culd – could; feal – feel; whiskas – whiskers; wud – would; freindly – friendly; larg – large; tale – tail; bak – back; gon – gone.

Home address

School address

Word Explorer

Name:

Year: Class:

Colour key (guide)

1	Blue	2	Dark Brown	3	Light Brown	4	Red
5	White	6	Black	7	Green		
8	Yellow	9	Orange	10	Pale Green		

❑ Write any new words you have learned.

Treasure Test 1

❑ Can you spell these words on your empty Treasure Chest sheet? Ask a friend to test you on them. Remember! Look, say, cover, write, check.
Write each word three times. Every time you get it right, colour in a gold coin on the Treasure Chest sheet.

come   day   the   dog

big   mum   no   dad

all   get   in   went

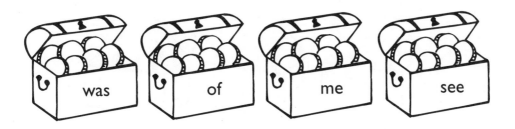

was   of   me   see

❑ Write the ones you find tricky in your Word Explorer.

Treasure Test 2

❏ Can you spell these words on your empty Treasure Chest sheet? Ask a friend to test you on them. Remember! Look, say, cover, write, check.

Write each word three times. Every time you get it right, colour in a gold coin on the Treasure Chest sheet.

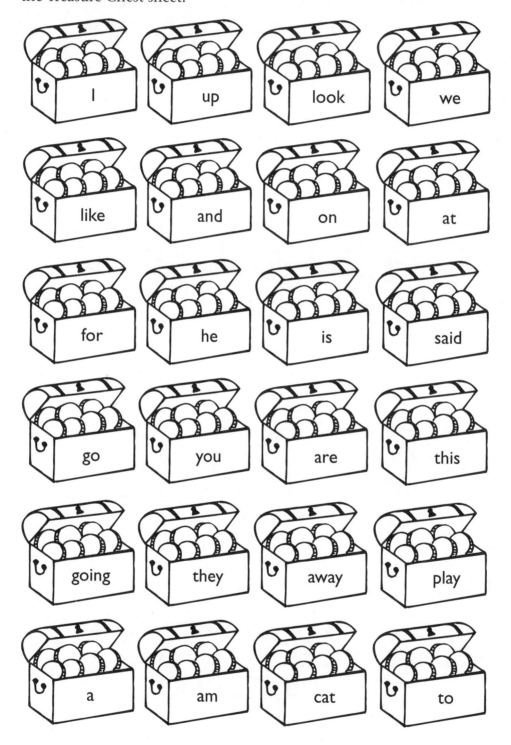

❏ Write the ones you find tricky in your Word Explorer.

Let's get dressed

❏ Sort these words into two lists:

belt	glove	hand	trousers	sock	hat
foot	neck	scarf	waist	legs	head

My body

head
_____
_____
_____
_____
_____

My clothes

glove
_____
_____
_____
_____
_____

❏ Now sort the words into pairs.

foot
_____
_____
_____
_____
_____

sock
_____
_____
_____
_____
_____

❏ Now write your own lists.

Summer clothes

_____
_____
_____
_____

Winter clothes

_____
_____
_____
_____

❏ If you were going to a fancy dress party, who would you choose to be and what would you wear? Draw how you would look on the back of your sheet.

As time goes by

spring   Monday   Thursday   August

Tuesday   June   Wednesday

October   February

summer   December

Friday   May

January   winter   April

autumn   November

Saturday   September

March   July   Sunday

❏ Sort the words above into the right lists:

Days of the week	Seasons

Months of the year

❏ Now write out each list in the correct order:

M	S

J

Rainbow words

❏ Look at this puzzle. Can you find nine colours? Write them down when you find them.

b	l	a	c	k	g	r	e	y
r	p	u	w	b	r	o	w	n
p	u	r	p	l	e	f	h	g
i	m	e	l	u	e	h	i	n
n	o	d	n	e	n	i	t	j
k	x	v	q	p	k	r	e	s

1 _____

2 _____

3 _____

4 _____

5 _____

6 _____

7 _____

8 _____

9 _____

❏ Now choose the right colours from your list to complete these sentences:

1 Coal is _____.

2 Cherries are _____.

3 A zebra is _____ and _____.

4 Grass is _____.

5 The sky is _____.

❏ Choose the best colour word you can think of to fit each sentence:

1 My favourite rose has _____ petals.

2 The hen had _____ feathers.

3 The sand was a lovely _____ colour.

4 In the sky were fluffy, _____ clouds.

5 The British flag is _____, _____ and _____.

Word grid

tall	long
colourful	short
lovely	wide

Jumble in the jungle!

❏ Look at the words that are underlined. Using the words in the word grid, fill in each box with a word that means the same as the underlined word. You can only use each word once.

In the jungle some of the trees are <u>small</u> and some are <u>big</u>.

The monkeys use their <u>big</u> tails to help them swing from tree to tree.

The parrots have <u>nice</u>, <u>bright</u> feathers.

A <u>big</u> river is running through the jungle.

Have you used each word in the word grid once?
❏ Now colour in the picture.

What are these for?

An explorer opened his rucksack and found these objects inside it:

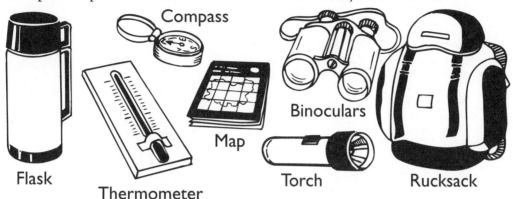

Compass

Binoculars

Map

Flask

Thermometer

Torch

Rucksack

❑ Use a dictionary to look up each word. Then complete these sentences:

1 The explorer uses the thermometer to ——————————

————————————————————————————

2 The binoculars will help the explorer to ——————————

————————————————————————————

3 The explorer will use the torch when——————————

————————————————————————————

4 The map will be used to ——————————————

————————————————————————————

5 The flask is used ——————————————————

————————————————————————————

6 The explorer needs the compass——————————————

————————————————————————————

❑ Underline the correct word to complete these sentences:

1 To find the word **thermometer** I would turn to the
beginning/middle/end of a dictionary.

2 To find the word **binoculars** I would turn to the
beginning/middle/end of a dictionary.

Mystery words

❏ See if you can work out the meanings of the mystery words by looking at how they are used in the sentences. Then check in a dictionary to see if you are right.

The explorer seldom had a wash.

What does **seldom** mean?

_____

_____

The wild pigs were grazing on nuts found on the forest floor.

What does **grazing** mean?

_____

_____

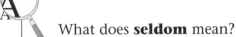

The aroma of the flowers was very strong.

What does **aroma** mean?

_____

_____

The plumage of the humming-birds glinted in the sunlight.

What does **plumage** mean?

_____

_____

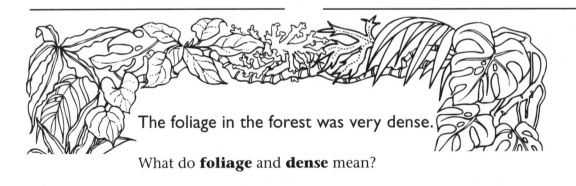

The foliage in the forest was very dense.

What do **foliage** and **dense** mean?

_____   _____

_____   _____

_____   _____

S S Sort it!

a b c d e f g h i j k l m
n o p q r s t u v w x y z

Words in a dictionary are written in alphabetical order. To place words in alphabetical order, look at the first letter of each word.

❏ Arrange the words on the leaves in alphabetical order:

a _____   g _____

b _____   h _____

c _____   i _____

d _____   j _____

e _____   k _____

f _____   l _____

❏ Write down some words to finish the list:

m _____   t _____

n _____   u _____

o _____   v _____

p _____   w _____

q _____   x _____

r _____   y _____

s _____   z _____

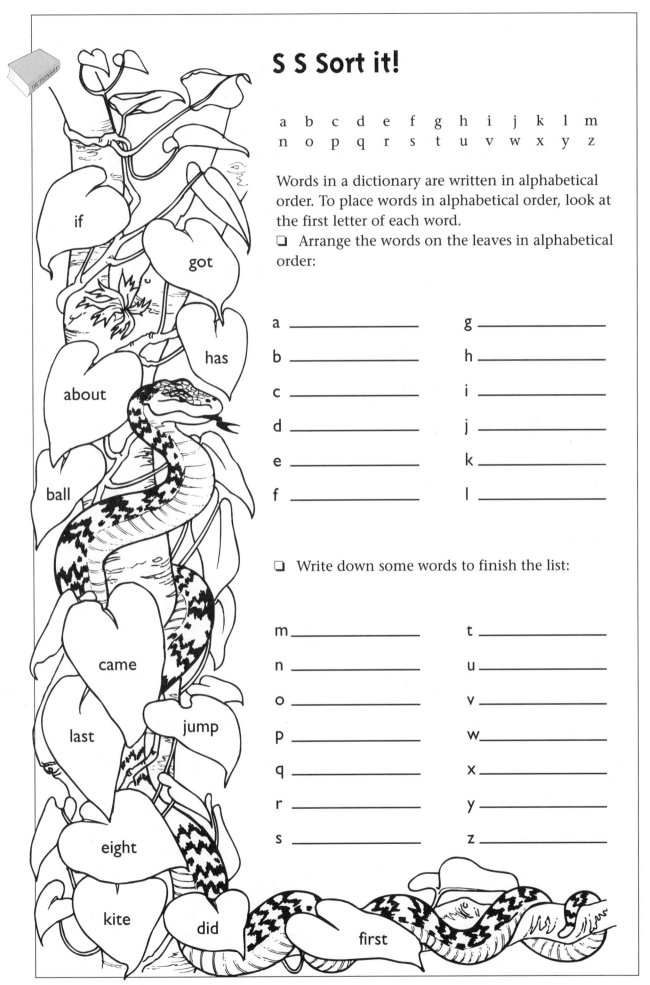

if
got
has
about
ball
came
last
jump
eight
kite
did
first

Alpha-bites

If words begin with the same letter, look at the second letters.

❏ Write the words on the bananas in alphabetical order.

boy

biscuit

banana

bed

bun

1 _____

2 _____

3 _____

4 _____

5 _____

❏ Write the food words on the monkey's tummy.

❏ Think of some more food words beginning with **b**. Write them in your Word Explorer.

Animal noises

Some words have double letters. Double letters are the same letter next to each other, such as:

sna**pp**ing

❏ Underline the double letters in these words:

chattering   buzzing   purring   hissing

❏ Look at the sentences below. Fill in the name of the animal and the sound it makes, using the words above.

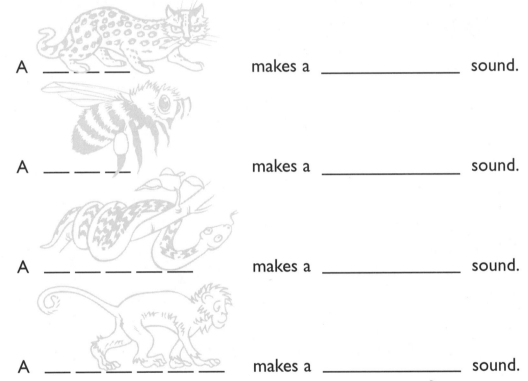

A ___ ___ ___   makes a _____ sound.

A ___ ___ ___   makes a _____ sound.

A ___ ___ ___ ___   makes a _____ sound.

A ___ ___ ___ ___ ___   makes a _____ sound.

❏ Now put these double letters in the right place:

ee   tt   pp

The frog ho ___ ___ ed into the pond.

The tiger was cr ___ ___ ping through the forest.

The birds were flu ___ ___ ering their wings in the trees.

Animal anagrams

An anagram is a word in which all the letters have been jumbled up.

birabt   =   rabbit

❏ Using the pictures to help you, work out these animal anagrams. Write the name of the animal underneath each picture.

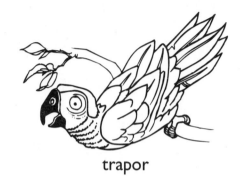

trapor

_____

ytlbufert

_____

lirloagat

_____

igrllao

_____

❏ Look at the animal words again. Each of the words has a double letter. This is when a word has two letters which are the same, next to each other, such as **rabbit**.

❏ Find the double letters in all the animal words and underline them.

❏ Now write down three other animal anagrams for your friend to solve!

A body of verbs

A verb is an action word.
It tells us:
what is being done (in the present)
or what has been done (in the past)
or what will be done (in the future).

❏ Look at the list of verbs ending with **-ing** at the bottom of the page
and choose the right verb to match each picture.

_____   _____

_____   _____

_____   _____

_____   _____

_____   _____

_____   _____

-ing verbs				
shouting	dancing	kissing	pointing	sitting
jumping	waving	kneeling	crying	thinking
carrying	laughing	catching	hugging	kicking

Now and then, big and small

❏ Fill in the spaces using words from the pictures. Some have been done for you. The words underlined are action words (verbs). The words in boxes are naming words (nouns).

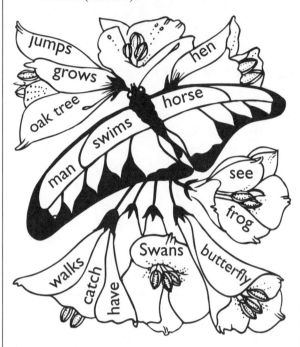

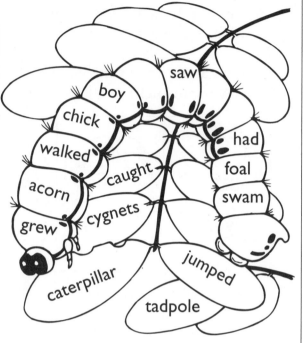

Present (now)

I I <u>see</u> a (man) digging in the garden.

2 The [　　　　] <u>swims</u> in the muddy pool.

3 A brown [　　　　] <u>walks</u> around the farmyard.

4 A big (oak tree) _____ in the park.

5 A glossy, brown (horse) _____ over the gate.

6 I often <u>catch</u> a [　　　　] in my net.

7 [　　　　] usually _____ lovely white feathers.

Past (then)

I I _____ a (boy) planting seeds.

2 The (tadpole) _____ in the pond.

3 A yellow (chick) _____ into the hen-house.

4 A tiny [　　　　] <u>grew</u> into an oak.

5 A small, brown [　　　　] _____ over the fence.

6 The bird _____ a small, green [　　　　].

7 The small (cygnets) _____ grey feathers.

Mini-crosswords

idney Snake is looking for synonyms!

Synonyms are words that have the same meaning. **Mini** and **small** are synonyms.
They can be made into a mini-crossword, like this:

s			
m	i	n	i
a			
l			
l	t		

Can you complete the missing synonym?

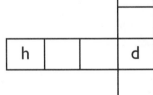

❑ Now choose from these words to complete these mini-crosswords:
discoverer, hard, walk, fresh, traveller, sturdy, roam, new

1

		f		
m	o	d	e	r	n
				w

2

w	a	n	d	e	r
					o
k					

3

| | s | t | r | o | n | g |
| h | | d | |

4

| t | | v | e | | | r |

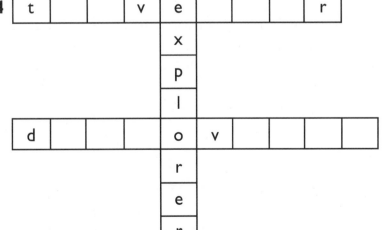

❑ Look in your thesaurus to see if you can find other synonyms for these words.

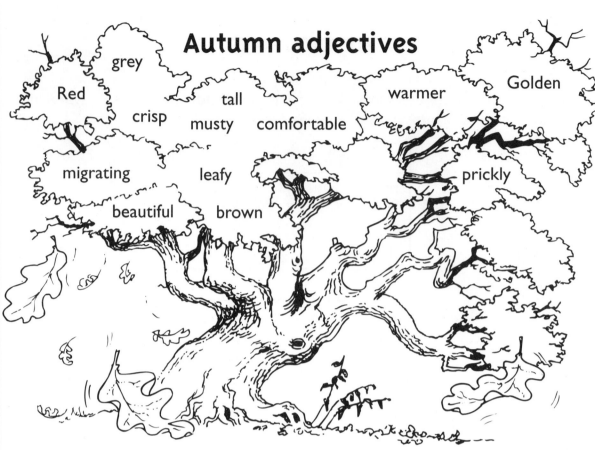

Autumn adjectives

grey

Red

tall

crisp

musty comfortable

warmer

Golden

migrating leafy

prickly

beautiful brown

Adjectives are describing words.

❏ Look at the adjectives in the tree. Then fit them into the correct places in the passage below which describes the season of autumn. Look out for those words beginning with a capital letter. It shows that they come at the start of a sentence.

It was a _____ day in autumn. _____ rays of

sunlight shone through the _____ trees.

A _____ squirrel scurried through the _____

branches, collecting acorns to store in his _____ drey.

_____ and _____ leaves fluttered slowly down

to make a _____ carpet on the ground.

A _____ hedgehog was beginning to prepare for

hibernation. There was a _____ smell in the air and, in

the sky, flocks of _____ birds were making their way to

_____ lands.

Friend or foe?

Parrot <u>said</u>, "There is going to be a great battle between the animals and the birds."

Bat asked, "Why are they going to fight?"

Parrot replied, "We birds believe we should rule the earth."

"I have wings. I must be a bird. I'll fight on your side," promised Bat.

The battle began and the animals were winning.

"I will change sides for, after all, I do have the body of a mouse," shouted Bat to the animals.

"So you will be no friend of ours!" exclaimed Parrot.

The birds turned on the bat.

"You must never fly with us again," squawked Parrot.

And that is why, even today, Bat flies at night.

❑ Underline in red the words that let the reader know that somebody was going to speak. The first one has been done for you.

❑ Underline in blue the words that let the reader know that somebody had stopped speaking.

❑ Do you know any more speech words? Look in your reading book. Write them in your Word Explorer.

All change

A prefix can change the meaning of a word.

The opposite of happy is **un**happy.

un is the prefix.

The opposite of  appear is  **dis**appear.

dis is the prefix.

 ❑ Spot the right and wrong words! Put a tick next to the words which are right and a cross next to the words which are wrong. Then write the correct words in the table below. Two examples have been done for you.

diswise ✗   disuse

dismount

unwise ✓   diseven

disdress

unuse

undress

un	**dis**
<u>unwise</u>	<u>dishonest</u>
un _____	dis _____
un _____	
	dis _____
un _____	
un _____	dis _____

uneven

unmount

disfriendly

unfriendly

untrust

untidy

distidy

dishonest ✓

distrust

unhonest ✗

Treasure Test 1

❏ Can you spell these words on your empty Treasure Chest sheet? Ask a friend to test you on them. Remember! Look, say, cover, write, check.

Write each word three times. Every time you get it right, colour in a gold coin on the Treasure Chest sheet.

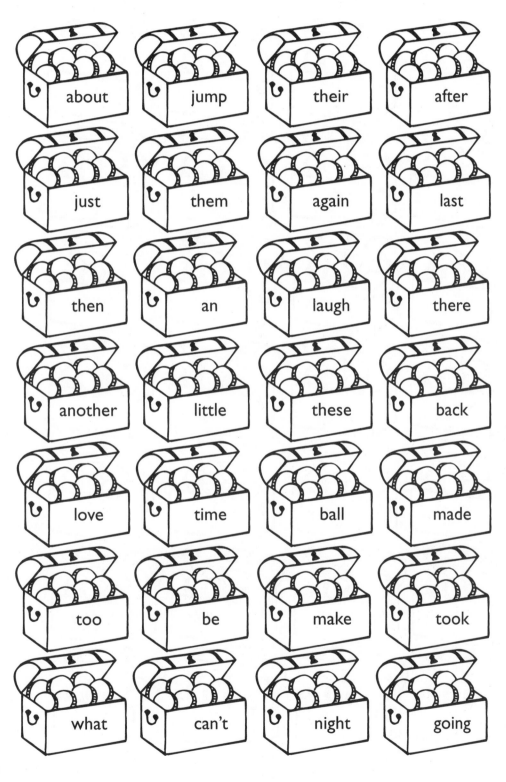

about	jump	their	after
just	them	again	last
then	an	laugh	there
another	little	these	back
love	time	ball	made
too	be	make	took
what	can't	night	going

❏ Write the ones you find tricky in your Word Explorer.

Treasure Test 2

❑ Can you spell these words on your empty Treasure Chest sheet? Ask a friend to test you on them. Remember! Look, say, cover, write, check.
Write each one three times. Every time you get it right, colour in a gold coin on the Treasure Chest sheet.

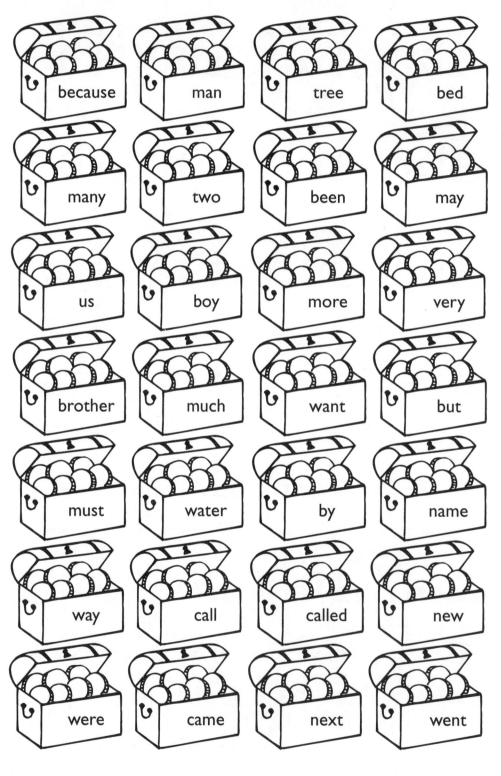

because   man   tree   bed

many   two   been   may

us   boy   more   very

brother   much   want   but

must   water   by   name

way   call   called   new

were   came   next   went

❑ Write the ones you find tricky in your Word Explorer.

Winter adjectives

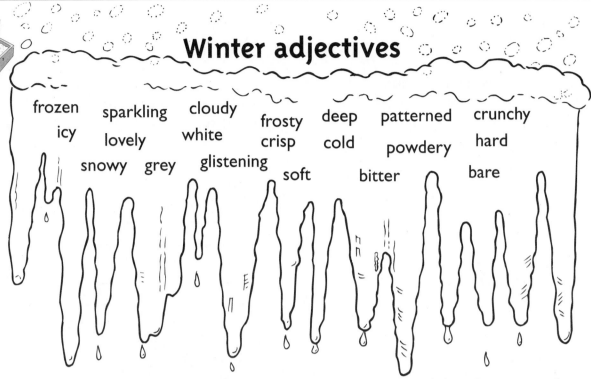

frozen   sparkling   cloudy   frosty   deep   patterned   crunchy
icy   lovely   white   crisp   cold   powdery   hard
snowy   grey   glistening   soft   bitter   bare

❏ Write a description of a winter scene. You can use some of the adjectives in the icicles and others that you think of.

Here are some nouns that you might use in your description:

December	snow	icicle	pond	window
January	sleet	snowflake	lake	chimney
February	wind	footprint	garden	hedge
Christmas	rain	track	sky	rooftop
	clouds	branches	trees	

Winter scene

_____

_____

_____

_____

_____

_____

_____

Grammar check

Definitions are the meanings of words.
Can you remember the definitions of words used in English grammar?

❑ Link each grammar word to its meaning. The first one has been done for you.

Definition	A single item
Sentence	An action word
Noun	A group of letters added to the end of a word that changes its meaning
Singular	A group of words that makes sense, and begins with a capital letter and ends with a full stop, question mark or exclamation mark
Prefix	The meaning of a word
Suffix	A word that describes a noun
Plural	A group of letters that can be placed at the beginning of a word to change its meaning
Adjective	A naming word
Verb	More than one

Discovering definitions

Here are some definitions. What are they describing?

1 An item of furniture with four legs and a back.

This is a _ _ _ _ _

2 A method of transport with three wheels, two pedals and a saddle.

This is a _ _ _ _ _ _ _ _

3 A machine that tells the time, found on a wall or a shelf.

This is a _ _ _ _ _

4 A very heavy animal with a huge mouth that eats plants. It spends a lot of time in water.

This is a _ _ _ _ _ _ _ _ _ _ _ _

5 A ball-shaped fruit with a thick skin. It has segments and pips.

This is an _ _ _ _ _ _

6 Items of footwear that come up to just below the knee. They are made of rubber with thick soles.

These are _ _ _ _ _ _ _ _ _ _

_ _ _ _ _

❑ Can you find your answers in a dictionary? If you can, write down the dictionary definitions on the back of this sheet.
❑ Now write your own definitions for these items:

A banana is _____

_____

_____

A cat is _____

_____

_____

Wing words

Homonyms are words that sound the same but have different meanings.
❑ Find the pairs of matching words and write them on the butterflies, as in number 1.

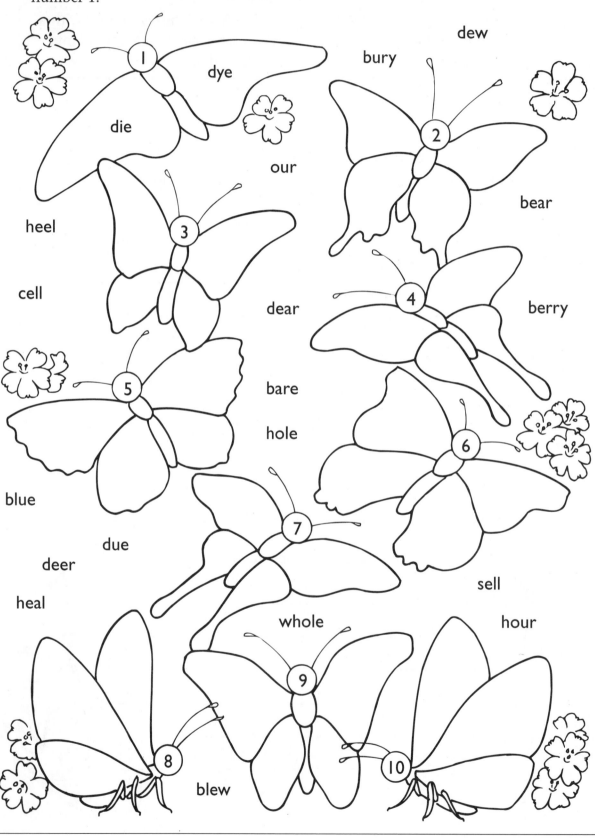

dye

die

dew

bury

our

heel

bear

cell

dear

berry

bare

hole

blue

due

deer

sell

heal

whole

hour

blew

Tiger twins

❏ Read these sentences then underline the homonym in the bracket that fits the sentence. (If you are not sure of the meaning of any words, use a dictionary to check.)

1 The explorer heard a (moan/mown).

2 He (knew/new) the sound was nearby.

3 He (sore/saw) a tiger behind a tree.

4 The tiger was in (pain/pane).

5 The tiger had been searching for (pray/prey).

6 It had been about to (slay/sleigh) an antelope.

7 The tiger had not caught the (sent/scent) of the hunter.

8 It was a very sad (seen/scene).

9 The tiger was very (week/weak).

10 The hunter hurried to get (some/sum) help.

❏ Write a sentence using each of these words:

Soar _____

_____

Sore _____

_____

The clues are there!

❏ Add the right noun for each of these adjectives. Use the pictures to help you work out the answers.

a slithering _____

a lumbering _____

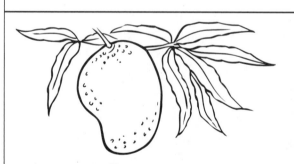

a snapping _____

a colourful _____

❏ Now think of an adjective to go with each of these nouns:

a _____ fruit

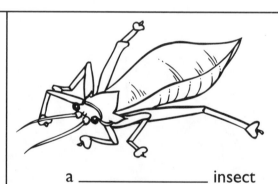

a _____ insect

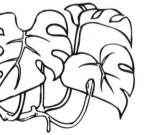

a _____ plant

a _____ frog

Robinson Crusoe

A noun is a naming word. An adjective describes a noun.
❏ Read this passage. Find the nouns and adjectives.
Underline the nouns in red and the adjectives in blue.

Robinson Crusoe's sailing ship was wrecked on a lonely desert island and he was washed ashore onto silver sands. He made himself a comfortable home in the rocky caves. He also made a strong raft using palm trees from the dense forest nearby. Using the raft, he was able to collect dry food and useful tools from the sinking wreck. With a sharp axe he built a tall fence to protect himself from fierce animals.

Now he made plans to feed himself. He collected juicy grapes and ripe bananas from the green forest and planted plump grains of rice and wheat he had found on the ship. Later he trapped wild goats which he used for fresh meat and creamy milk.

❏ Choose four of the nouns and draw them in the boxes below.

Inside and outside

❏ Join the words below to make new words.

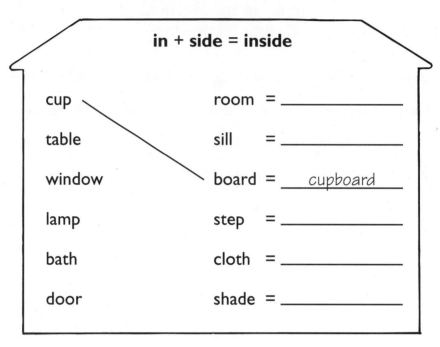

in + side = inside

cup   room = _____

table   sill   = _____

window   board = *cupboard*

lamp   step   = _____

bath   cloth = _____

door   shade = _____

out + side = outside

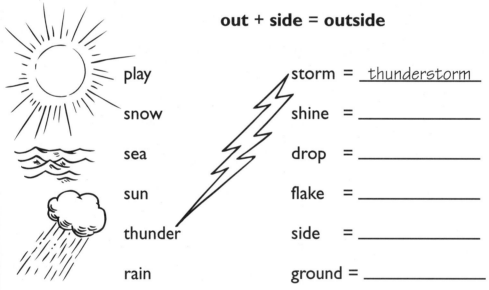

play   storm = *thunderstorm*

snow   shine = _____

sea   drop   = _____

sun   flake   = _____

thunder   side   = _____

rain   ground = _____

❏ Now think of some other words you could join to these words to make new words.

house _____   home _____   earth _____

after _____   day _____   some _____

sea _____   tooth _____   light _____

Singular and plural (1)

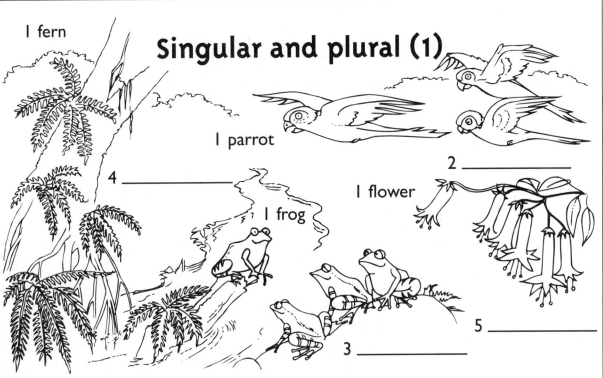

I fern

I parrot

I flower

I frog

4 _____

2 _____

3 _____

5 _____

❏ The singular nouns have been written down already. Write the plurals in the spaces provided.

❏ Complete this sentence:

To change the singular words into their plurals I have had to add an _____.

❏ Colour in the picture.

❏ Now change these nouns from singular to plural.

One bunch of flowers.

Three _____ of flowers

One broken glass

Four broken _____

One thorny branch

Two thorny _____

One cardboard box

Seven cardboard _____

One rose bush

Five rose _____

One sandy beach

Six sandy _____

❏ Complete this sentence:

I have had to add _____ to nouns ending in **ch**, **sh**, **ss** and **x**.

Singular and plural (2)

❏ Write down the plurals of each of these words. Think carefully!

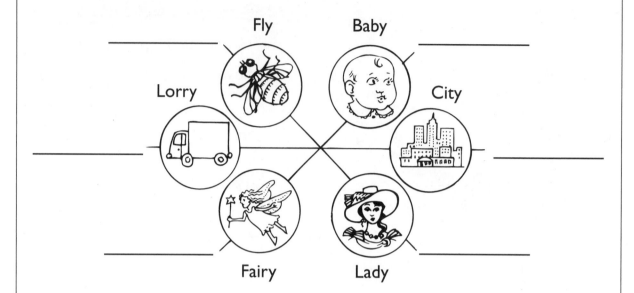

Fly   Baby

Lorry   City

Fairy   Lady

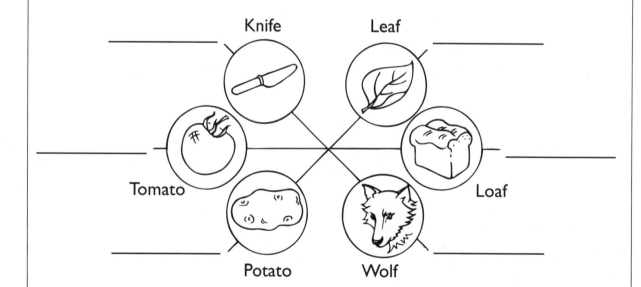

Knife   Leaf

Tomato   Loaf

Potato   Wolf

❏ Write the singular form of these nouns:

children   men   feet

_____   _____   _____

women   geese   teeth

_____   _____   _____

Message in a bottle

❏ Read this passage. Underline the words that end in **-le**.

Robinson Crusoe was in a bit of a muddle. He was stranded on a desert island. He tried to scramble to the top of the hill to see if any ships were passing by but he fell in a big puddle. One day he spotted a little bottle floating in the water. Instead of a message inside the bottle, he found a crossword puzzle.

❏ Can you help Robinson Crusoe finish the crossword?
All the answers end in **-le**.

Across
1 This is made of wax and helps you to see in the dark.
4 Another word for unbelievable.
6 You boil water in one of these.
7 You sit at this to eat your meals.
Down

1 A baby might be rocked in one of these.
2 A horse is kept in one of these.
3 A carrot is one of these.
5 A princess might live here.

Copycat!

Many words can mean the same thing.

BIG means the same as HUGE
tiny means the same as small

❏ Use the code to find words which have the same meaning:

A	B	C	D	E	F	G	H	I	J	K	L	M
1	2	3	4	5	6	7	8	9	10	11	12	13

N	O	P	Q	R	S	T	U	V	W	X	Y	Z
14	15	16	17	18	19	20	21	22	23	24	25	26

happy   ___   ___   ___   ___

        7   12   1   4

sad   ___   ___   ___   ___   ___   ___   ___

      21   14   8   1   16   16   25

shout   ___   ___   ___   ___

      25   5   12   12

great   ___   ___   ___   ___   ___   ___   ___   ___

      23   15   14   4   5   18   6   21   12

❏ Use the code to write matching words for:

strong

old

middle

You greedy monkey

In this story there are some contractions; this is where two words are shortened into one word by using an apostrophe.
☐ Find the contractions and then write out the words in full below.

1	2	3	4
5	6	7	8

1 I'm the cleverest monkey in the forest.

2 Can't we share your bananas?

3 I don't want to share.

4 I'll hide my bananas down by the river.

5 Who's that?

6 My bananas aren't as big as his.

7 The monkey reached out to steal the bigger bananas.

8 I shouldn't have been so greedy.

Oh! I've lost my bananas.

Re- or Pre-?

Prefixes are phonemes that have meanings.

Re can mean **again**.
Pre can mean **before**.

❏ Choose the correct prefix to make a new word in each sentence.
Cross out the wrong prefix.

1 I had to pre / re peat my spelling test.

2 The cook pre / re pared a delicious meal.

3 After a fire, the hospital had to be pre / re built.

4 Drive carefully to pre / re vent traffic accidents.

5 The house plant grew so huge that I had to pre / re pot it.

6 The doctor pre / re scribed some ointment to cure a rash.

7 The naughty children had to pre / re make their beds after they had bounced on them.

8 Pre / Re fixes can be found at the beginnings of words.

9 The fox escaped death because the farmer had to pause to pre / re load his gun.

❏ Check your new words by looking them up in a dictionary.

S-t-r-e-t-c-h

Suffixes

When we add **ful** to a word it means **full of**. When we add
ful to the end of a word, though, there is only one **l**.

❑ Add **ful** to these words and write a sentence for each one:

1 play _____ _____

2 mouth _____ _____

3 rest _____ _____

4 use _____ _____

When we add the suffix **less** it means **being without**.

❑ Add **less** to these words and write a sentence for each one:

5 care _____ _____

6 cheer _____ _____

7 fear _____ _____

8 spot _____ _____

When we add **ly** to a word it is usually an adverb. An adverb tells
us more about the verb. For example,

She spoke quietly.

❑ Add **ly** to these words and then write a sentence for each one:

9 quick _____ _____

10 loud _____ _____

11 brave _____ _____

12 bright _____ _____

Sssh! Silent letters

Some words begin with silent letters. When you say the word, the second letter is the one you hear first. For example:

kn sounds as **n**

gn sounds as **n**

wr sounds as **r**

❑ Decide whether **kn**, **gn** or **wr** should be placed at the beginning of these words:

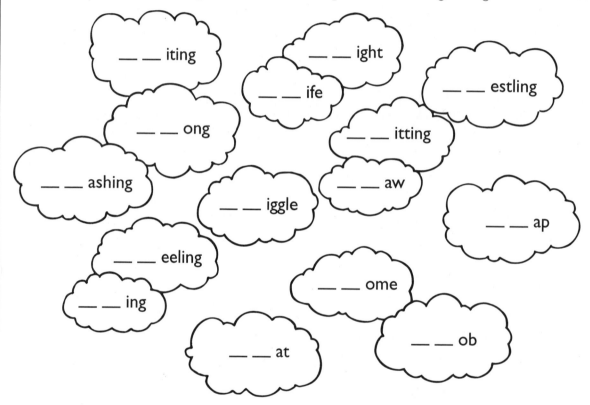

— — iting

— — ight

— — ife

— — estling

— — ong

— — itting

— — ashing

— — aw

— — iggle

— — ap

— — eeling

— — ome

— — ing

— — at

— — ob

❑ Use your dictionary to find more words that begin with a silent **k**, a silent **g** or a silent **w**.

_____   _____   _____

_____   _____   _____

Treasure Test 1

❏ Can you spell these words on your empty Treasure Chest sheet? Ask a friend to test you on them. Remember! Look, say, cover, write, check.

Write each word three times. Every time you get it right, colour in a gold coin on the Treasure Chest sheet.

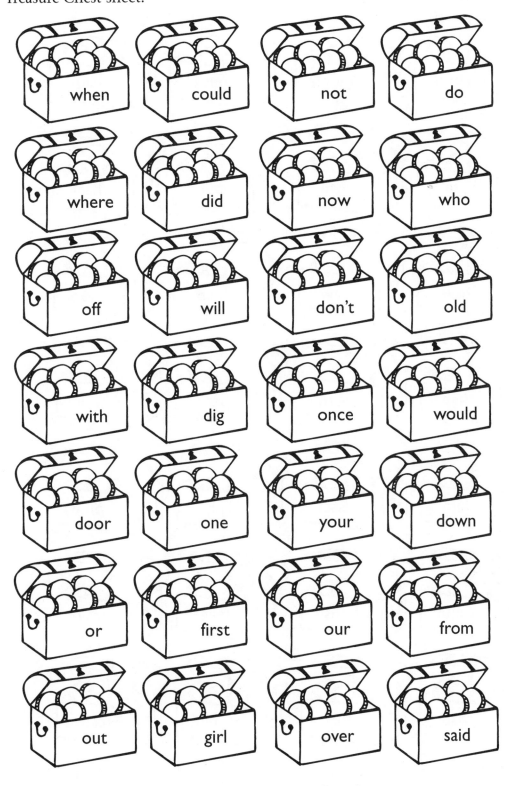

 ❏ Write the ones you find tricky in your Word Explorer.

Treasure Test 2

Can you spell these words on your empty Treasure Chest sheet? Ask a friend to test you on them. Remember! Look, say, cover, write, check.

Write each word three times. Every time you get it right, colour in a gold coin on the Treasure Chest sheet.

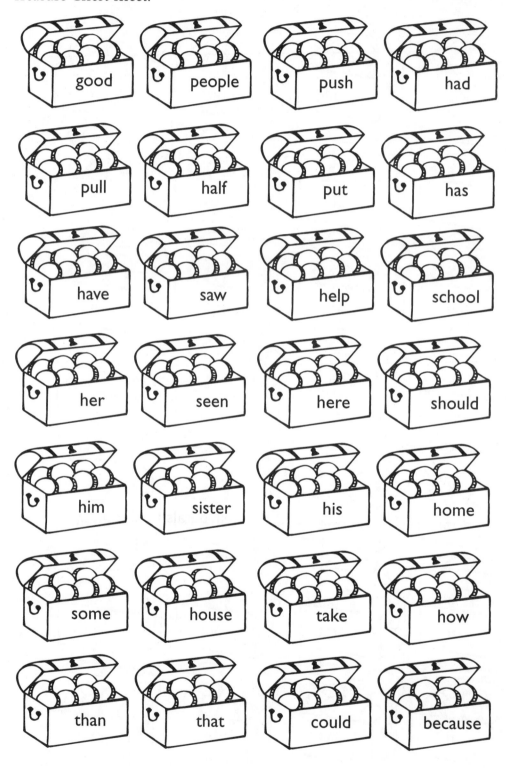

good people push had

pull half put has

have saw help school

her seen here should

him sister his home

some house take how

than that could because

❏ Write the ones you find tricky in your Word Explorer!

Spot the word

words on leopard's spots: hurried, chattered, crept, boomed, fall, opened, shining, slithered, singing, crawled

❏ Fill in the spaces in this passage using the right words from the leopard's spots:

It was a very hot day in the rainforest. Birds were _____

sweetly up above. Snakes _____ among the roots of the

trees. Monkeys _____ as they swung from branch to

branch. Large spiders _____ through the grasses.

Colourful flowers _____ their petals to the bright sun.

A leopard _____ along after its prey.

 Suddenly, thunder _____ in the sky and raindrops began

to _____, slowly at first and then quickly. Soon all the

glossy, green leaves were _____ and the creatures of the

forest _____ to their hiding places.

Making faces – more adjectives

Adjectives are describing words.

❑ Choose suitable adjectives from the box below to complete these sentences:

Anna has a _____ face, with

_____ hair and a _____ mouth.

She looks _____. Her nose is

_____.

Sophie has _____, _____ hair and a

_____, _____ mouth. She looks

_____. Her cheeks are _____.

Ashley is _____. Someone has made him very angry.

He has a _____ face, _____ cheeks and

_____ ears. His hair is _____ and

_____.

Chandani has a _____ face. She

has _____, _____ hair

and _____ eyes.

Adjectives			
curly	smiling	furious	narrow
short	long	happy	round
pretty	freckled	sad	large
tiny	plaited	plump	drooping
straight	spiked	sparkling	pointed

Get into your groups!

These root words have lost their prefixes:

_____lead   _____-operate ★   _____tend ★

_____body   _____port   _____take ★

_____-education   _____septic ★   _____change

_____place   _____-exist   _____social

❏ Use your dictionary to make new words by adding these prefixes to the root words: **ex-**, **mis-**, **co-**, **anti-**. Then add the words to the box below.

ex-	mis-	co-	anti-

❏ Write the meanings of the new words marked with a star ★:

★ _____operate _____

_____

★ _____tend _____

_____

★ _____septic _____

_____

★ _____take _____

_____

Delving in the dictionary

❏ Choose three interesting scientific words from the science topic that you are doing now.

| Word 1 | Word 2 | Word 3 |

❏ Now find three different dictionaries. Write down the different dictionary entries for each of your words.

Dictionary A Word 1	**Dictionary B** Word 1	**Dictionary C** Word 1
Word 2	Word 2	Word 2
Word 3	Word 3	Word 3

❏ Highlight scientific information for each word in blue. Highlight all other information in green.

Which dictionary do you think gives the best information? Why?

Well said!

❑ Cut out the starred boxes below (keep them safe!). Stick one of them over the word **said** in each sentence. Remember to choose the most suitable starred word!

1 "Fe, Fi, Fo, Fum! I smell the blood of an Englishman!"

| said | the angry giant.

2 "Keep still, or the eagle will fly away," | said | the bird watcher.

3 The toddler | said | , "I've cut my knee and it hurts!"

4 "We've won The World Cup!" | said | the football fans.

5 "Stand still! You are nearly at the edge of the cliff!" | said |

my Dad.

6 "Can you come out for a bike ride today?" | said | Emma, from

across the road.

7 "I've won the painting competition!" | said | Mark excitedly.

8 "I would have won if I had taken part,"

| said | Tracey, under her breath.

9 The teacher | said | to us that we had done well in our tests.

10 "That's the funniest joke that I have heard in ages," | said | my

Uncle Tony.

| roared | called | squealed | whispered | reported |
| yelled | cheered | muttered | cried | laughed |

Word picture puzzles

Some words look and sound the same, but have different meanings:

The lizard sat on the <u>rock</u>.

Don't <u>rock</u> the boat.

 ❏ Use the picture clues to help you find the same word for each pair of sentences:

1 If I look at my _____ I can tell you what the time is.

I love to _____ the frogs jumping into the water.

2 That man is cutting down the tree with a _____

I _____ a girl and a boy next to the waterfall.

3 The boy ran up the grassy _____

I want to put my money in the _____

❏ Now write your own sentences. First look at the pictures to help you work out what the word is. Then put the word into two different sentences. Make sure the word means something different in each sentence!

 = w __ __ __

1 _____

2 _____

 = s __ __ __ __

1 _____

2 _____

Getting the message across

❑ Can you work out the meanings of these short, everyday sayings? Write each saying inside the triangle in which it belongs.

Good afternoon   Go away   No   How do you do?

Wow!   Pardon me   What!

Look out!   Hello   It can't be   Beware

Watch it!   I'd rather not   Excuse me   Good morning

Welcome   Oh dear

Take care   Well I never!   Hi!   Not really   Ta!   I'm sorry

Pleased to meet you   Much appreciated   Really?

Oh no!

A warning   **A surprise**   **Thank you**

An apology   **A disappointment**   **A greeting**   **A refusal**

Star turn

A prefix is a syllable that comes at the beginning of a word. It gives a clue to the meaning of the word.

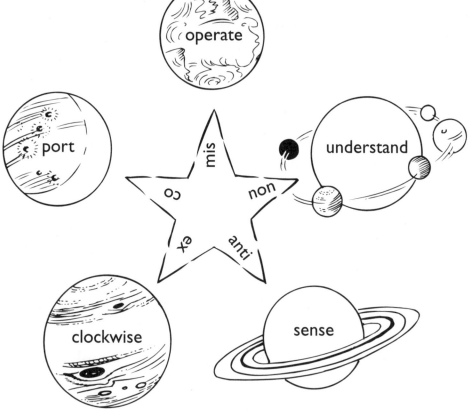

❏ Match the points of the star to the planets to make new words. Write the words below, then find their definitions in your dictionary.

1 _____ _____

_____

2 _____ _____

_____

3 _____ _____

_____

4 _____ _____

_____

5 _____ _____

_____

Back to our roots

Prefixes	Root word		New word
dis	mortal	→	_____
mis	sense	→	_____
un	noon	→	_____
im	pleased	→	*displeased*
non	regular	→	_____
after	fortune	→	_____
ir	lucky	→	_____

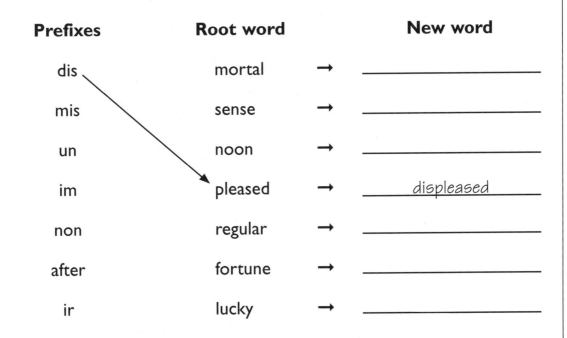

❏ Draw arrows to link each prefix to a root word.
❏ Write each new word in a sentence. Use your dictionary to help you.

1 _____

_____

2 _____

_____

3 _____

_____

4 _____

_____

5 _____

_____

6 _____

_____

7 _____

_____

Take my place

All these words are pronouns:

him   it   she   he   they   them

A pronoun can be used instead of a noun.

<u>Jasvinder and Susan</u> went to the park.

<u>They</u> went to the park.

❑ Replace the underlined words with pronouns:

[   ]

There is no way we can go without <u>Renu and Sarah</u>.

[   ]

Have you seen <u>John</u>?

[   ]

<u>Nicola</u> took the book back to school.

[   ]

Don't try to push the door open, you might break <u>the door</u>.

❑ Now look at this passage. Change the underlined words into pronouns:

[   ]

Ryan was going to meet Simon after school. <u>Ryan and Simon</u> wanted

to play football before they went home to have their tea, but Simon

[   ]

had left the ball in the car. How could <u>Ryan and Simon</u> play football

[   ]

without <u>the ball</u>? Perhaps the teacher, Mrs Cooke, might lend them a

[   ]

ball. <u>Mrs Cooke</u> kept a football in her classroom. Do you think she let

[   ]

<u>Ryan and Simon</u> borrow it?

People and pronouns

The words that have been underlined are called pronouns. Pronouns can be used in a sentence instead of the names of people.

❏ Write down the pronouns you can see on this page.

<u>He</u> _____ _____ _____ _____

❏ Now look at these sentences. Write in your own names for people in place of the pronouns.

<u>He</u> will take the dog for a walk today.

<u>She</u> enjoys going to the park.

I told <u>them</u> to put their toys away but they didn't listen!

Yes, I am going to see <u>him</u> at the football stadium tonight.

<u>She</u> says that school finishes at about half-past three.

<u>They</u> should enjoy going to the cinema to see the film about dinosaurs.

❏ Now make up some of your own sentences using these pronouns:

1 they _____

_____

2 she _____

_____

3 he _____

_____

4 them _____

_____

Bridge that gap

A conjunction joins two sentences together to make a longer sentence. Here are some words that can be used as conjunctions:

if	so	while	though
since	when	but	until

❏ Make each pair of sentences into one sentence using a conjunction. The first one has been done for you.

1 I like to fish.   The weather is warm.

   I like to fish **when** the weather is warm.

2 I enjoy fishing.   I am not very patient.

_____

3 You may see a kingfisher.   You are lucky.

_____

4 My dog waits patiently.   I prepare my fishing line.

_____

5 My dog likes to accompany me.   He can run along the bank.

_____

6 I stay in my pitch.   I catch a fish.

_____

7 Fish feed best at dawn.   My best catch was in the evening.

_____

8 My brother has not been with me. He tripped over my fishing line.

_____

Linking words

❏ Choose a conjunction from those written in the leaves to complete the sentences below. Try not to use the same one twice.

while

then

if

since

I The explorer sat down to look at the map

_____ he had lost his way.

though

and

2 A beautiful tiger sheltered under a large tree

_____ the rain poured down.

as

because

3 The monkeys would chatter noisily

_____ they sensed danger.

4 Overhead the sky was dark and dull

when

but

_____ there was a rumble of thunder

in the distance.

5 Ants busily collected leaves from the ground

_____ the parrots squawked loudly in

the trees up above.

6 The explorer was very hot and tired

_____ he had not stopped to rest all day.

7 The leopard would have to run very fast to catch its

prey _____ it would not be easy in the heat.

Animal alliterations (1)

Alliteration is when a sound is repeated within a group of words to give an interesting effect. Here is an alliterative sentence:

Mischievous **m**onkeys **m**oved among the treetops.

❑ Can you match each animal name to an adjective which alliterates? The first one has been done for you.

mischievous	bees
slithering	**m**onkeys
stinging	dragonflies
spinning	lizards
crawling	snakes
darting	crocodile
lazy	chimpanzees
angry	scorpion
prickly	butterflies
beautiful	alligator
buzzing	porcupines
chattering	spiders

Animal alliterations (2)

❏ Using some of the pairs of alliterations from the worksheet 'Animal alliterations (1)', add the subjects and adjectives to the following sentences. Then lightly shade the alliterative sound in each sentence. For example:

Mischievous **m**onkeys **m**oved among the treetops.

I _____ _____ fluttered among the bright flowers.

2 An _____ _____ attacked its anxious prey.

3 _____ _____ move silently among the swaying grasses.

4 A _____ _____ scuttled across the desert sand.

5 _____ _____ lie sleeping in the sun.

6 _____ _____ suspended themselves from their silky webs.

7 _____ _____ protect themselves with their spiny quills.

8 _____ _____ cling to the canopy of leafy branches.

Use your head

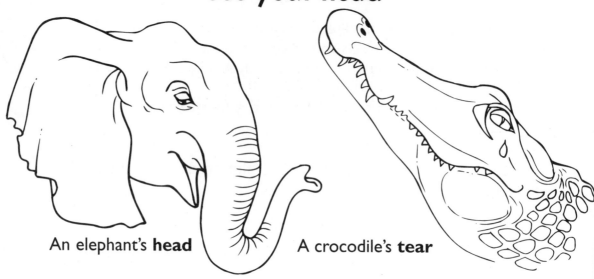

An elephant's **head**   A crocodile's **tear**

Both of the words in bold print contain **ea**, but they sound very different.

❑ Read these words:

ear	bread	dead	fear	lead
hear	tread	dear	dread	year

❑ If they sound like **head** write them in the elephant's head.
❑ If they sound like **tear** write them in the crocodile's tear.

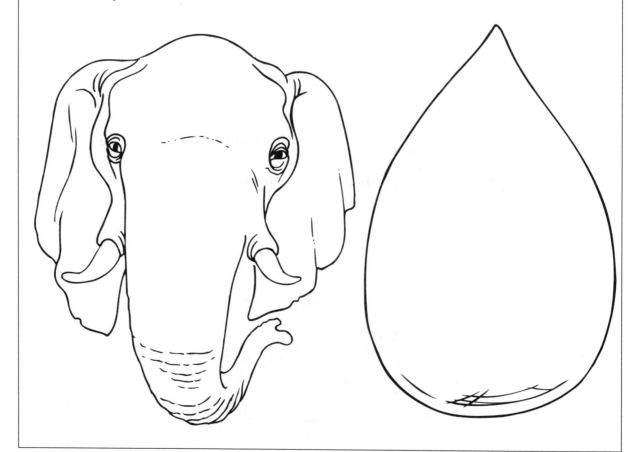

How well can you spell?

In this passage there are 20 spelling mistakes. Look carefully to see if you can find them all.

❑ Put a circle around any spellings that you think are wrong. Check the spellings and meanings in your dictionary. Write the correct spellings underneath the passage.

The strange creature

The litle mouse ran quickly along the path. He was searching four food in the forrest. After a while, he spotted somethink creeping slowley along the river banck. What was it? It was makeing a very funny sound whatever it was! As it got closer, the mouse thort it mite be a cat.

Oh dear! To his dismay, the strange creature sore him and ran over towards the frightened mouse. The tiny mouse was too scard to move. He culd feal the strange creature's whiskas tickling his ears. Surely now he wud be pounced on and eaten!

But to his surprise, the strange creature gave him a freindly nudge with his cold nose. The mouse opened his eyes to see a larg curious otter. Then, with a flick of his tale, the otter scampered off, on his way bak towards the river. With a loud splash he was gon!

Spelling corrections

little _____ _____ _____

_____ _____ _____ _____

_____ _____ _____ _____

_____ _____ _____ _____

_____ _____ _____ _____

Treasure Chest